Listening skills
for
Busy People

By Dr Peter Kaye
MA FRCP MRCGP

Published by   EPL Publications
                      41 Park Avenue North
                      Northampton
                      NN3 2HT

© Peter Kaye, 2006

ISBN 0 9539825 0 5

First published 2006

A CIP catalogue record for this book
is available from the British Library

Contents

Introduction

The ordinary human skills of listening to those close by have been lost in the cacophony of noise and the rush of technological life ... If listening skills are practised and developed through experience, the very process of opening up communication between people will often provide effective help. Enabling a person to speak freely, to express their fears, to distinguish facts from feelings, to test the reality of their assumptions and providing an opportunity to put the different aspects of a problem 'on the table' rather than keeping them tangled up within – all these facets can help people towards finding workable solutions"

Michael Jacobs, 1985
Swift to Hear

Giving attention and receiving attention are fundamental human needs. We are social animals – we need to make meaningful social connections with others.

And yet receiving attention is much easier than giving it. If we want to learn how to give attention we need to train ourselves.

There is more to active listening than waiting to speak. Active listening is a form of hospitality. It is making space in our schedule for the concerns of others. It demands energy and commitment, but it does not have to be unduly time-consuming.

A doctor with advanced cancer said to a group of medical students, "Give me just 10 minutes of interested, uninterrupted listening, and I'll tell you all you need to know to help me."

Active listening is a very useful skill in many areas of life and helpful in many different roles (doctors, nurses, social workers, counsellors, policemen, solicitors, clergy, teachers, salesmen, managers, hairdressers, journalists and many others). A survey, conducted by the University of Pittsburgh's Katz Business School, showed communication skills are the single most important factor in choosing managers.

Listening well enables us to influence, persuade, negotiate, gain information, understand others, solve problems, share interest, see how another person feels, show support, avoid conflicts and misunderstandings, and goes a long way toward creating good relationships.

Giving undivided attention and recognizing individuality tends to enhance a person's self-esteem.

Listening skills versus listening

Listening skills are different from listening. Imagine buying a new TV set. In order to watch a programme you first need to connect it up and tune the various controls (channel, volume, contrast, brightness, colour). Once the controls are correctly tuned you can ignore them, and concentrate on the programme. The control knobs are like your listening skills. Once you are tuned in correctly to the other person you can forget about how you do it and simply focus on the programme. The important thing is the programme (the conversation) but you need to be able to tune in (use listening skills) first.

Listening versus Counselling

Listening is different from counselling. Counselling certainly requires the skills of active listening, but they are different.

Active Listening provides a person with an opportunity to think more clearly, to be heard and to tell their story.

Counselling involves a planned series of conversations to help a person understand their emotional responses to a particular experience (e.g. bereavement, divorce). It requires constant supervision and self-awareness to prevent personal emotions from affecting the process.

Psychotherapy is similar to counselling but involves a longer series of conversations to help a person develop new insights and to change their thinking and behaviour.

Improving our ability to listen is a lifelong quest, and one that requires daily practice and daily learning. It is a useful skill to develop because it can improve our own personal relationships and quality of life, as well as our ability to perform many worthwhile tasks.

But reading a book about how to listen well is a bit like reading a book about how to swim well – you only begin to really understand once you get into the water. Becoming a better listener is always a work in process.

I am very grateful to Peter Bailey, Sancha Barlow, Emily Kaye, David Smart and Martin Steele for their helpful comments.

> **KEY POINT:** We have two ears and one mouth to remind us that we are meant to listen twice as much as we speak.

"SEEN-AS-EASY"

*"We think we listen but we don't. We finish each other's
sentences, we interrupt each other, we moan together, we fill in
the pauses with our own stories, we look at our watches, we sigh,
frown, tap our finger, read the newspaper, or walk away. We
give advice, give advice, give advice"*

Nancy Kline, 1999
Time to Think

Social Listening is something we all do. Because of this,
listening is seen as easy. We all listen, all the time. Or do we?
How much of what we say is to tell our own story or justify
our position, rather than being a true response to another
person? Active Listening is very different to Social Listening.

Social Listening is a 2-way exchange whereas Active
Listening is mostly one way.

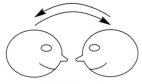

Social Listening

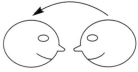

Active Listening

The phrase "Seen-As-Easy" provides a useful checklist of
the main skills of active listening.

SEEN = Non-verbal skills

S = **S**etting
E = **E**ngaging
E = **E**ye Contact
N = **N**oticing minimal cues

AS = Attitude

A = **A**ccepting the other
S = **S**elf-awareness

EASY = Verbal skills

E = **E**choing
A = **A**sk questions
S = **S**ilence
Y = Empath**Y**

'SEEN' relates to non-verbal skills. The word "SOFTEN" is also a useful mnemonic for the basic non-verbal skills of listening: *Smile* (but not so it is interpreted as derision), *Open* body-posture (avoid crossing arms and legs), *Forward* lean slightly (but don't invade personal space), *Touch* (can be empathic, but use very sparingly and be aware it can get misinterpreted), *Eye contact* and *Nods*.

'AS' relates to the underlying non-judgemental *acceptance* of the other person (even if you don't like what they say) and the *self awareness* to reduce your own inner concerns to make space for the other person's concerns ("self-as-small").

'EASY' relates to the essential verbal skills for responding to the other person, using *echoing, asking questions, silences* and the skill of *empathy*.

The best social listening is when *both* people use the skills of active listening to explore each other's minds. This is very rare. Social listening at its best has been beautifully described by Theodore Zeldin in his book *Conversation*.

> *"Creativity usually needs to be fueled by more than polite chat. Simply talking does not necessarily change ones own or other people's feelings and ideas. The kind of conversation I am interested in is one in which you start with a willingness to emerge a slightly different person. It is always an experiment whose results are never guaranteed. It involves risk. It is an adventure in which we agree to look at the world together and make it taste less bitter. Conversation is not just about conveying information or sharing emotions, or just a way of putting ideas into people's heads. Conversation is a meeting of minds with different memories and habits. When minds meet they don't just exchange facts, they transform them, re-shape them, draw different implications from them, engage in new trains of thought. Conversation doesn't just re-shuffle the cards, it creates new cards. It's like a spark that two minds create ..."*

> Theordore Zeldin, 1998
> *Conversation*

KEY POINT: "Seen-As-Easy" provides a checklist of listening skills

A Model for Active Listening

"It is only theory that decides what we manage to observe"
Albert Einstein (1879–1955)

"All thinking involves theories — it is practical and scientific to examine them"
P. Alderson, 1998
The importance of theories in healthcare

"There is nothing so practical as a good theory"
Kurt Lewin (1890–1947)

The purpose of communication is to get a message across to others, to convey thoughts and ideas effectively – and yet this is surprisingly difficult.

This simple model emphasizes that in active listening the speaker and the listener are doing fundamentally different things. The speaker is encouraged to remember, reflect and express feelings, whilst the listener attempts not to do this, but to focus as much as possible on the other person. The aim is to provide the speaker with a safe space to hear themselves and to reflect on their own words.

> *"All of us have our own individual language. When you listen to a person you should listen knowing that he or she is speaking an alien language and that you should not try to understand in terms of your language."*
> Sydney Rosen, 1982.

In order to think about the process of listening, it is helpful to break down the interaction into stages, and then consider what happens at each stage.

A Model of Listening
A model provides a way of identifying and describing the important elements in a complex system. A conversation can be broken down into a number of transactions. During any transaction we do 3 things: we speak, we listen (both to our own words and those of the other person) and we think.

A MODEL FOR LISTENING

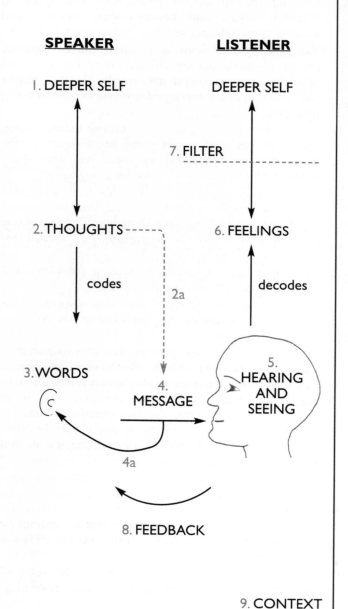

SPEAKER

LISTENER

1. DEEPER SELF

DEEPER SELF

7. FILTER

2. THOUGHTS

6. FEELINGS

codes

2a

decodes

3. WORDS

4.
MESSAGE

5.
HEARING
AND
SEEING

4a

8. FEEDBACK

9. CONTEXT

1. The "deeper self" (memories, beliefs, aspirations) influences current thoughts and feelings. During active listening the speaker is given time and space to maximize connections between their thoughts and words and their deeper self.

2. Thoughts arise from a combination of internal triggers (from the deeper self) and external triggers. The thoughts are then coded into words. (2a the speaker may also adapt their message according to their ongoing thoughts).

3. Words form in the speaker's mind just before talking, but these "thought words" may be different to the words that are verbalized out loud. We often speak before we know exactly what we are going to say.

4. The message is conveyed in words (and non-verbal behaviour) and the speaker also hears their own words, which may differ from their thoughts. When someone pays attention to their own words they can "meet themselves" at a deeper level (4a).

5. The message is received by hearing the words and observing the behaviour of the sender.

6. The message is decoded and this involves interpretation by the listener (of both the words and their emotional content).

7. The internal filter of the listener aims to minimise input from their deeper self which serves to distract. The speaker and the listener have fundamentally different internal processes. The speaker is encouraged to link to their deeper self, whereas the listener aims to filter out their own assumptions, judgments, and beliefs. In active listening the aim is to reduce internal distractions and focus on the speaker.

8. Feedback from the listener is important because what someone says and what someone else hears can be amazingly different! Feedback avoids making incorrect assumptions. It is sometimes important to summarize or repeat what you think you heard and ask, "Have I understood you correctly?"

9. The context (privacy, comfort, expectations, rules of an organization, culture of an organization) powerfully affect the process of listening.

Barriers to Active Listening

"The job of the professional is to be a midwife for a person's concern – to get those concerns out and on to the table as quickly as possible".

Peter Maguire

When listening, we can inadvertently set up barriers that prevent a person divulging their problems to us. These include:
- Wrong context
- Focusing on our own concerns
- Poor feedback
- Internal barriers

Wrong context
The context of listening can act as a barrier because of either external factors or cultural factors.

External factors: include such things as lack of time, noise, distractions, deafness.

Cultural factors: include such things as wrong clothing, rigid attitudes of seniors, fear of being blamed for upsetting a person or a culture of the organization ("we don't discuss such things").

Focusing on our own concerns
In active listening the focus needs to be on the feelings of the other person. We must avoid being self-focused or giving advice or discussing personal issues.

	SELF-FOCUSED	OTHER-FOCUSED
FACT-ORIENTATED	Advice	Explanation
FEELINGS-ORIENTATED	Manipulation	Active Listening

There are ways of improving our ability to focus on the other person, discussed further in Skill 6: Self-Awareness.

Poor feedback
The words we choose when giving feedback can inhibit the process of active listening. Some problems when giving

12

feedback include: using jargon, using different types of words to the other person, using stereotyped comments ("I understand"), changing the subject, interruptions, multiple questions (confusing), asking the same question twice, requesting explanations (being nosy) and language problems.

Listeners may also unconsciously use "blocking tactics" to protect themselves from their own emotions, or the fear of unleashing emotion in the other person. These include: *normalizing*, *premature reassurance*, *ignoring* and *selective attention*.

Internal Barriers
Inner distractions (coming from our own thoughts and feelings) need to be recognised and held in check by the self-aware listener. The listener's personal thoughts should rarely be verbalized, which can prevent active listening to the other person's concerns. Mentioning personal feelings or memories can occasionally be helpful, provided the aim is always to enable the other person to feel more at ease and to talk more easily about their own issues (not yours).

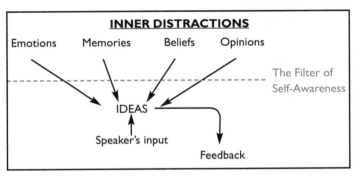

Inner distractions include: emotional reactions ("that makes me feel very angry"), private side tracks ("that reminds me of ..."), counter-arguments ("I don't agree because ..."), confusion ("that does not fit my frame of reference"), imaging ("perhaps he means ..."), judging ("I don't approve of ...") or feeling dislike for a person.

KEY POINT: You are NOT listening when: you are in a hurry or you think about yourself or you don't ask any questions or you assume you know what I'm going to say or you over-react to certain words or you feel critical.

Skill 1: Setting

- Setting
- Engaging
- Eye contact
- Noticing non-verbal cues

- Accepting the other
- Self-awareness

- Echoing
- Asking questions
- Silence
- EmpathY

"There is evidence to suggest that the way nurses communicate may depend on the environment created by the ward sister"

Wilkinson, 1991

Before we start listening we have to pay attention to the setting, which can be described in terms of:

- – Physical space
- – Time boundaries
- – Social context
- – The culture of an organization

Physical space includes:

- Chairs (at same level?)
- Quiet (mobiles off)
- Privacy – no interruptions
- Comfort (warm enough? clean? light? ventilated?)
- Lay out of chairs/furniture
- Smell of room
- Ambience of room (full of office equipment?)

Time Boundaries enable conversations to be held more safely, in the knowledge that there is a clear time to end. Verbalize clear boundaries at the start ("We can talk together for 20 minutes now and if necessary we can meet again tomorrow afternoon.") and remind the person of the time boundary near the end (eg "we have 5 minutes left together, is there anything else you want to talk about?"). Setting aside specific time for active listening often improves the quality of listening. It is possible to spend a lot of time with a person and never listen properly.

- – When will we meet? (eg Monday, 5pm)
- – Length of session? (eg 20 mins)
- – How often? (eg Just once, then review)

Be realistic about your time limitations but always keep a promise to return.

Time boundaries are important even in a single session of active listening, to give the person some guidance about how much time you are offering, eg "We have 45 minutes together, what would you like to discuss?" A time boundary is also important because a sensitive issue may be deliberately held back until a few minutes before the end of a session (when it feels safer to mention it). This can only happen if a clear time for ending has been agreed. In the counselling setting a clear time boundary enables the ending of regular sessions to be discussed which can be especially important if endings (and loss) are areas of concern.

The Social Context (place, family, work, friends, etc) might remain unspoken but it can affect the dialogue. Consider:

-   Is this the right place?
-   Are you the right person to do the listening?
-   Is confidentiality an issue? (eg you might know their family)
-   Social role? (yours and theirs).

The culture of an organization affects the quality of listening. Training in communication skills may not be enough to change the way you listen, for example if the boss has let it be known that people should not be seen "just standing around chatting". A good example is the culture of a hospital ward which greatly affects the quality of listening ("Sister doesn't like to see us just sitting with patients"; "the consultant does not like us to discuss their diagnosis with the patients"). The culture of an organization is best defined as "the way we do things around here" and (because of the power of social pressure) it can cause massive invisible resistance to speaking, listening or thinking. This is why training programmes in communication skills usually have little impact on an organization, unless senior people get involved and there is real commitment to continued learning and change.

> **KEY POINT:** External factors such as time pressure, place and social context all affect how a person feels and therefore affect what a person says

Skill 2: Engaging the other person

- Setting
- Engaging
- **Eye contact**
- **Noticing non-verbal cues**
- **Accepting the other**
- **Self-awareness**
- **Echoing**
- **Asking questions**
- **Silence**
- **Empath**Y

Mirroring

"You intentionally adjust your own behaviour so that it more nearly ressembles those aspects of the other person which you have particularly noticed – delivery of speech, tone of voice, posture, gestures – so that someone observing the pair would be struck by the similarities"

Roger Neighbour, 1987
The Inner Consultation

Engaging with a person means concentrating on the here-and-now. Engaging requires 3 things:

- – Establishing rapport
- – Concentration
- – Observing the other person.

Establishing rapport is initially done non verbally by *smiling*, *eye contact*, *posture* and *proximity*, and *mirroring* (vocal pattern, posture). It is usually best to sit down. By sitting down with a person it signals our intention to offer real depth of listening. We use the phrase 'on the level' to mean a shared openness.

Smiling and eye contact are especially important for building rapport and encouraging the person to talk.

But non-verbal rapport is not enough. We have all known those cocktail party moments when we are skilfully conveying our intent to listen (nodding, smiling, eye contact) but our concentration has drifted, and suddenly we have missed a chunk of the conversation. (We then nod and smile vigorously to cover up.) Establishing non-verbal rapport is only the first step.

Concentration is needed because we think (and read) faster than we speak. People speak at around 3 words per second, but we can take in up to 12 words a second. Since only a part of our mind is needed to pay attention to spoken words, it is easy to go into mind drift – thinking about other things while listening to someone.

It is essential to admit to lapses ("my concentration slipped then. I'm sorry, I was distracted for a moment and was not listening properly – can you repeat what you just said?"). This demonstrates we are listening to the best of our ability.

Concentration needs extra energy if a speaker is difficult to follow or has voice problems, or uses dialect or odd words.

Concentration needs mental alertness which is helped by physical fitness and by re-positioning of the body, the limbs and the head from time to time.

Note-taking to remember key points (using either headings or a mind-map diagram) can be appropriate in some situations.

Observing the other person can help reduce distractions from our internal dialogue. If you lose concentration, redirect your attention to the person's minimal cues. Just notice them carefully. Think of yourself as a video camera. This re-establishes your attention firmly back onto the person in front of you.

Don't try to interpret the non-verbal cues, just notice them. The amount of information conveyed by cues is too great to analyse (left brain); but simply observing the other person very carefully (right brain) allows your intuition to interpret the complex cues in the best way. The process of observing the other person blocks your own inner dialogue and makes you concentrate on what the patient is telling you.

Mirroring the posture and behaviour of the other person increases rapport (and when there is already rapport, mirroring tends to occur automatically)

KEY POINT: Engagement involves concentrating and this is helped by carefully observing a person's non-verbal cues.

Skill 3: Eye contact

"When you are listening, keep your eyes on their eyes. Don't look away unless there is a fire or you have a seriously unsavoury personal emergency"

Nancy Kline, 1999
Time to Think

Eyes are the focal point of the body. Infants as young as 3–4 weeks respond particularly to a pair of eyes. Seeing 'eye-to-eye' is a basis for communication. Skilled listeners gaze at the speaker's face 60–70% of the time – a bit less when speaking (40% of time), a bit more when listening (85% of time).

Eye contact is better termed "mutual gaze" referring to the time spent looking at the face area (usually in glances of 2–3 seconds). Mutual glances of 1.5 seconds occur 30% of the time on average.

Gaze that meets 60–70% of the time indicates good rapport.

Like most body language, the length of time that one person gazes at another is culturally determined.*

In addition to noticing the gaze of another person we subconsciously notice pupil size. The pupils signal our emotions. The pupils dilate if excited, thinking, aroused or in low light, which can look appealing ("big baby eyes") and constrict if angry or in a negative mood ("beady eyes").

Increased gaze can signal either liking (pupils dilated) or hostility (pupils constricted).

Eye contact is complex because it is both a channel to receive messages and also a way of sending signals. We use gaze not just to gather information but to synchronize conversations (especially greetings and partings); to express attitudes to others and to act as a social reinforcer. An eye flash may signal aggression or flirtation (depending on other signals).

---

* Latin Americans and Southern Europeans look more at each other than the British or white Americans, black Americans look less.

Professional gaze
is directed on the forehead
and creates a serious
atmosphere

The Social gaze
is between a person's eyes
and mouth and creates a
social atmosphere

Intimate gaze
extends below the chin and
creates an intimate
atmosphere

Mutual gaze gives a feeling of intimacy and openness. Those who look more are seen as more attentive, friendly, competent and interested. People look more at those they like (although 100% gaze is uncomfortable for both). Gaze may be reduced by feelings of dishonesty, anxiety, despair or if difficult topics are discussed.

Looking downwards more than usual may be associated with sadness, embarrassment, low self-esteem or shame. Looking away (whether a person is speaking or is silent) usually means that person is thinking hard and does not want to be interrupted yet. Neuro-linguistic programming (NLP) teaches that the different directions of a person's gaze co-relate with different types of thought, such as verbalizing, remembering, visualizing – but it is easier to find out what a person is thinking by simply asking them.

Eye closure for longer than a second, especially if repeated, signals that the person wants to block you out (they may feel upset, bored, superior, threatened ...). Normal blink rate is about one every 10 seconds (increased by anxiety, reduced by thinking).

KEY POINT: Skilled listeners gaze at the speaker's face at least 60–70% of the time

Skill 4: Noticing non-verbal cues

- Setting
- Engaging
- Eye contact
- Notice non-verbal cues
- Accepting the other
- Self-awareness
- Echoing
- Asking questions
- Silence
- EmpathY

"We concentrate so hard on words and forget that our movements, postures and gestures are telling their own story. Actions become gestures and gestures transmit messages"

Desmond Morris, 1997
(Manwatching)

"When you catch your mind wandering, watch the minimal cues like a hawk"

Roger Neighbour, 1987

Non-verbal signals are used to:

- Support speech (nods, glances, vocalization)
- Express emotion (eg sighs, head down, hands fidget)
- Communicate interpersonal attitudes (proximity, gaze).

Nonverbal cues are very powerful. The impact of words is not simply due to what we say, it's also conveyed by our behaviour as we "say" it.

Non-verbal signals (eye contact, facial expressions, gestures) are part of a rapid stream of signals moving in both directions. The sender is usually less aware of non-verbal communication than the receiver. With some communication (such as pupil size) both parties remain unaware, but the receiver may nevertheless be influenced.

| Person A | → encodes | NV Signal | → decodes (correctly or incorrectly) | Person B |

We may notice an individual signal but it is better to interpret clusters of signals, such as with your eyes, posture, body language, hand-shake, appearance and voice (tone of voice, loudness, pitch, speed of speaking). Non-verbal communication also includes such things as appearance, clothing, smell and the use of personal space (eg getting too close may signal aggression or flirtation, depending on other behaviour).

Noticing your cues

Skilled listeners are mindful of their own non-verbal cues, as well as the non-verbal cues of the other person. For example, are the chairs at the same height and are they arranged at an angle that is best for active listening?

Awareness of your own non-verbal behaviour is discussed further in the chapter on Self-Awareness.

Noticing their cues

When we use the phrase "his words had an impact", we usually mean it metaphorically. But we can in fact watch where our words make their impact. Is it in the speaker's eyes (widening , narrowing, moving or becoming still), or brow, or lower lip, or cheek muscles, or posture or gestures? Hand movements and breathing rate are particularly powerful indicators of emotion. Don't try to make 'sense' out of what you see – merely observe as accurately as you can and trust your own unconscious processes. Notice too the effects on your own emotions by using your observing self, eg "I suddenly feel very protective, I think she reminds me of my daughter" (see page 26).

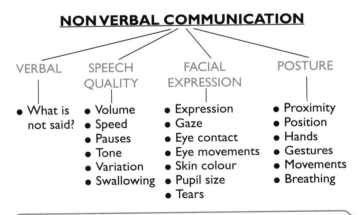

Skill 5: Accepting the other

- Setting
- Engaging
- Eye contact
- Noticing non-verbal cues
- Accepting the other
- Self-awareness
- Echoing
- Asking questions
- Silence
- EmpathY

"It is through the stories we tell ourselves and others that we live life. When we have made an experience or a chaos into a story we have transformed it, made sense of it, transmuted experience, domesticated the chaos"

Ben Okri, 1995
Birds of Heaven

"The act of telling the story is part of the healing activity"
John Launer, 2002
Narrative-based Primary Care

People only relax and talk openly if they feel liked and accepted, and although this is largely conveyed non-verbally, acceptance is greatly enhanced by thinking of the person's story as part of their wider life-story.

Listening can trigger prejudices within us. This is because the brain works by pattern recognition (part of a pattern rapidly calls up the whole pattern, allowing us to quickly recognize objects or name a tune from a few notes). But there is a problem with pattern recognition in that whenever we assume "this is the same as" it triggers a pattern which sets off emotions and stereotypes which can prevent us from really listening to the person in front of us. Our stereotyped thinking makes us think we understand their situation – we search for a similar pattern – and this can lead us into prejudices.

Focusing on a person's unique story can help us reduce our prejudices and increase our sense of acceptance without becoming distracted by our prejudices. Stories are important. They link events with meaning ("and then ...", "and that's why ...") allowing new connections to be made and evolving new understanding that allow us to make sense of our experiences.

Stories also engage our interest. When we tell or hear stories (using the pronoun 'I') about real situations it affects us emotionally, whereas when we talk in general terms ("people nowadays seem to think ...")it is often boring.

Stories get shaped by being told and heard. Imagine you are late for work because you witnessed an accident; your natural impulse is to tell people the story. If information gets added by others ("I heard about that on the radio – they said a man was killed") the story grows and becomes a shared story. In a similar way, each of us construct our own unique life-story, adding to it, repeating it, re-shaping it, keeping some bits, discarding others, re-membering it and eventually owning it as part of our own unique self.

Listening to stories and to a person's "biographical pain", (their sense that "life has not turned out the way I wanted") we hear not just about what happened, but *their story* about what happened. Listening to a person's story with a commitment to understanding how it feels to experience their life has been called "Empathic Witnessing" (Kleinman, 1998).

"MY STORY IS BROKEN, CAN YOU HELP ME FIX IT?"

Stories often carry some sense of being shipwrecked by the storm of life, when the present is not what the past was supposed to lead to. Events can turn a person into a "narrative wreck". Extending this metaphor, story-telling can repair the damage by redrawing maps and finding new destinations. Stories not only describe what we experienced, but give us an opportunity for a new experience: the telling of the story and its reception by another person. The person telling the story receives affirmation because they discover that their story is worth listening to by others. A person who can turn a crisis into a story transforms fate into experience. We can help a person out of their chaos by being a witness to their story.

drawn from Frank, 1995

KEY POINT: Acceptance is enhanced by listening to a person's story in terms of their whole life-story.

Skill 6: Self-awareness

- Setting
- Engaging
- Eye contact
- Noticing non-verbal cues
- Accepting the other
- Self-awareness
- Echoing
- Asking questions
- Silence
- EmpathY

"To grow in self-understanding involves becoming aware of what is happening within ... of the different levels of identity and the continuing need for integration. Recognising some of my own contradictions makes me more open and compassionate to others. This struck me once when a student told me, with a broad smile, of his inner despair – 'the smiling depression' doctors call it. I had often used that particular defence myself when depressed and had experienced the loneliness of it"

Anne Long, 1990
Listening

Good listening skills require a high level of self-awareness. One way to train yourself in increased awareness is to join a therapeutic group and ask for feedback, which can be a shock ("you stare at people, sometimes, as if you are beseeching them for something").

Awareness of our own body language

We tend to be unaware of the non-verbal signals we are sending. After I had been a GP a few months (and in the days before GPs used computers), a patient said "You are always in such a hurry". This was a surprise. I had imagined I was providing undivided attention. But I was signalling "I am in a hurry" by routinely checking my watch before I wrote an entry in the notes (because the date was on my watch). The patient saw me glancing at my watch and assumed I was checking the time. By becoming more aware of our non-verbal behaviour, we can make the other person more comfortable by selecting behaviour (posture, speed of speech) that fits with and resonates their own ("mirroring").

A good way to see your own signals is to use a video camera during an interview.

Awareness of our own words

Our words need to match those of the speaker. It is easy to slip in words relating to your own experiences or feelings – this needs to be avoided. If a speaker uses a particular word (eg tumour) it is often unwise to use a different word ("It was bad enough having a tumour, now you're telling me I have a cancer as well"!). Paraphrasing or summarizing what someone has been saying, using their own words or similar words, demonstrates listening, especially if you have held it in your memory for a time.

Awareness of our inner dialogue

We never stop thinking. One way of becoming aware of this is to try and stop it. Sit in a chair in a quiet room with no distractions for 20 minutes and quieten your mind. It can't be done! Similarly, when we are listening our own memories and feelings constantly intrude into the space that is meant for the other person and interfere with the process of active listening.

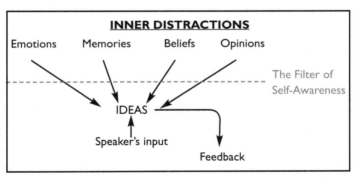

Skilled listeners prepare for active listening by regularly giving themselves time to listen to their own inner concerns and to reflect on them. Even 10 minutes a day makes a considerable difference. This practice creates an "inner space" for the concerns of others. It means that when your own thoughts or emotions intrude, it is easier to ignore them, because you have already given them some attention. A good way of quietening the inner distractions and making yourself focus on the other person is to turn your attention to observing the other person's non-verbal cues. This is discussed further in Skill 5: Accepting the other.

Awareness of our observing self

In addition to the background chatter of our inner dialogue, we humans have the mysterious and amazing ability to step back inside our mind and use an inner observing self to reflect on our inner dialogue. This observing self is highly active in the skilled listener, monitoring and registering the external dialogue and simultaneously monitoring and controlling the inner dialogue. Active listening is guided by comments and observations from our inner observing self. We are doing several things at once when we listen with real attention (listening, making connections observing body language ...), which is why it takes up so much energy to listen well.

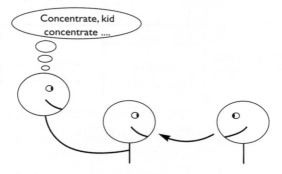

Awareness of our own emotions

The more aware we are of our own emotions the less likely they are to contaminate the listening space created for another person. Becoming aware of our own emotions can involve hard work. John Hull, who went blind, described the value of listening to his own voice as he talked about his feelings, to help him process and understand what emotions he was going through. He used a tape recorder to listen over and over to his own words.

> *"In June 1983, about two and a half years after I had been registered as a blind person, I began to record on cassette my daily experiences. This was when the truth of being blind began to hit me. **There are emotions so profound that you don't feel anything.** Recording the experiences of being blind helped me to recognize what the emotions were because if I then played the little passage back to myself, it would make me feel something when I listened to it."*

John Hull, 1990

Increasing our self-awareness

The Johari Window is a useful awareness model of how we relate to others. We can increase our self-awareness by increasing our openness with others.

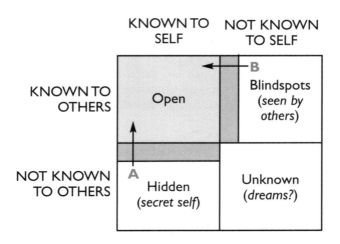

Increasing our openness can be achieved by self-disclosure (sharing our thoughts) and by requesting feedback.

A Self-disclosure (telling stories that start with "I") reveals some of the hidden part of yourself to another, and increases the Open area between two people. Children share their inner selves more naturally than adults.

   NB. Self disclosure can increase intimacy but over-disclosure can be embarrassing – balance is needed.

B Feedback from an observer can enable you to become more aware of your blindspots (eg "Do you realize you walk in a stooped position")

   NB. Feedback is only usually helpful if it is requested and given in a supportive and a non-threatening way, and at the right time. Methods include use of videos or "360 degree" appraisals from others in an organization.

> **KEY POINT:** Good listening requires a high level of self-awareness.

Skill 7: Echoing

- Setting
- Engaging
- Eye contact
- Noticing non-verbal cues

- Accepting the other
- Self-awareness

- Echoing
- Asking questions
- Silence
- EmpathY

"This procedure of echoing saves you spending time wondering what to say in the next sentence. You are not supposed to spend time constructing wise and significant questions; you must concentrate instead on listening intensely to what the person says.".

T. Bendix, 1982
The Anxious Patient

Echoing refers to a technique of listening best described by the psychiatrist Torben Bendix in his book "The Anxious Patient". As the listener, you simply repeat a key word or phrase used by the person, usually turning it into a question. It sounds simplistic but it works. It makes you focus on the words of the other person instead of the words in your head. For example:

[S = Speaker;   L = Listener.]

S – *It happened suddenly*

L – *Suddenly?*

S – *Yes, when I was in the car coming home from work*

L – *Coming home from work?*

S – *Yes, I remember it vividly*

L – *You remember it vividly?*

S – *Yes, it was just as I turned a corner that I saw my friend's car parked by the road. It was such a shock.*

L – *It felt a shock?*

S – *The car shouldn't have been there.*

L – *Shouldn't have ...?*

S – *My friend was meant to be abroad, and I suddenly realized it meant something was going on.*

L – *Going on?*

S – *With my wife. An affair.*

In the unlikely event that the person says it feels annoying that you keep repeating their words, you can explain "it is because I feel we should focus on exactly what you are telling me". Echoing does two things:

1. Echoing increases the chances of eliciting a person's real problems which is a key skill of active listening in many settings. Each time you echo a phrase you are really saying "Can you say a bit more about ...?". This tracks the conversational cues, a bit like a dog tracking a scent, and quickly leads to the relevant issues. This also reduces the need to ask "How did you feel?", because by focusing on what happened, the feelings inevitably emerge.

2. Echoing is also a very useful first step in demonstrating empathy, an attempt at understanding the other person's experience and feelings, which is the most therapeutic part of active listening, discussed in more detail in Skill 10: Empathy.

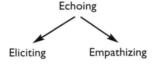

Echoing of non-sequiturs is especially important. Non-sequiturs are words or phrases that seem to have no connection to the present conversation. But illogical or seemingly irrelevant comments are motivated by something. Such comments link directly to important subconscious issues, and are entirely logical in terms of the person's inner world. Noticing them and echoing them will often lead to important new connections and insights.

NB. Note that echoing is not necessary if a person is freely telling their story.

KEY POINT: Echoing focuses the attention of the listener on the words of the speaker (instead of the words in his own head).

Skill 8: Asking Questions

- Setting
- Engaging
- Eye contact
- Noticing non-verbal cues
- Accepting the other
- Self-awareness
- Echoing
- Asking questions
- Silence
- EmpathY

"Don't ask picky, clarifying or confirming questions unless you are so confused that you feel faint"
Nancy Kline, 1999

"The possibilities that can be destroyed by playing a game of questions and answers are innumerable."
Torben Bendix , 1982
The Anxious Patient

Questions are important when listening because they show interest, but they must be used sparingly. A question almost always leads to the other person answering it (with the exception of experienced politicians!) which changes the direction of a conversation.

So the problem with questions is that they tend to lead the conversation into fruitless directions, because the direction was chosen by you, rather than the other person..

Open questions (eg starting "What ...?", "How ...?") tend to *open up* the dialogue and enable the other person to control the conversation. Closed questions (eg starting "Did you ...?", "Have you ...?") tend to *direct* the dialogue and can be used to give inapporpriate advice. The principle is to use mainly open questions during active listening and to use them sparingly and skilfully. Closed questions (which lead to 'yes' or 'no' answers) are only occasionally used to deliberately change the direction of a conversation.

---

7 USEFUL QUESTIONS
FOR ACTIVE LISTENING

● What happened? (hearing the story)	– Prompting
● Can you say some more about that?	– Exploring
● Could you explain that again?	– Clarifying
● May I see if I have understood you correctly ...?	– Checking
● What is the connection between ...?	– Linking
● Could you repeat what you just said?	– Emphasizing
● How would you summarize what we have discussed?	– Summarizing
● How did/does that make you feel?	– Empathizing

"Why?"

The question "why?" needs to be used very sparingly in active listening because we are often meeting our own needs out of curiosity. We need to make our "why?" questions useful to the other person. The main value in asking "why?" is to notice a discrepancy between different aspects of a conversation. This can result in real emotions being expressed (eg "I noticed earlier you said ... whereas just now you said ..."). Discrepancy can also occur between the words spoken and non-verbal communication (eg "You are talking of very sad things but you keep laughing – I am wondering why that is?).

"Do you want to discuss it now?"

Be sensitive, and consider using silence rather than questions. Detecting emotional distress does not mean the person wants or needs to discuss it now. The person may be very vulnerable to an over-intrusive curiosity about their emotions, especially by someone who is a skilled listener, which has been described as "mind rape" (Zigmund, 1978).

KEY POINT: Questions are very powerful and can change the direction of a conversation – use them sparingly.

Skill 9: Silence

- Setting
- Engaging
- Eye contact
- Noticing non-verbal cues
- Accepting the other
- Self-awareness
- Echoing
- Asking questions
- Silence
- Empath**Y**

"Pauses in a conversation do no harm"
Theodore Zeldin, 1998
Conversation

"Silence of the heart is more important than silence of the mouth. A man may seem to be silent, but if in his heart, he is condemning another he is babbling ceaselessly"
Henri Nouwen (1932–1996)

It is remarkably difficult to hold a silent space for another person. We live in an age of hurry and rush and instant gratification. Yet holding a silent space and giving another person a rare opportunity to reflect on what they have been saying (and to consider what they themselves think) is a rare gift. Silence is often the most valuable aspect of active listening.

There are four golden rules for active listening that all relate to the importance of 'holding' a silent space to enable the

---

4 GOLDEN RULES FOR ACTIVE LISTENING

1. If you don't know what to say, keep quiet.
2. Only interrupt a pause with the question "What were you thinking?"
3. Never answer questions.
4. Never give advice.

---

other person to think.

Do not answer questions, because they are not relevant to the task in active listening. Reflect them back eg "I wonder what makes you ask me that question?".

Allowing long pauses enables the other person to go at their own pace, to listen to their own words and to reflect on what they have just said ("how do I know what I feel until I hear what I say"). Allowing silences to occur can enable a person to analyze their thoughts and feelings to make new links or new discoveries about how they think or react, or to come to new insights.

Silence must be friendly and relaxed; signal that the silence is comfortable by smiling, nodding and looking relaxed.

After a period of silence, the question "What were you thinking about?" often brings up a relevant topic for discussion.

Watch the other person's eyes during a silence. If their eyes are darting from side to side, or if they continue to look away, it signals that they are thinking. Leave them to it.

Crying is a form of silence (because the words stop for a while) and it is also a visual clue that something important has been touched on. Don't waste the opportunity by being over-respectful of the tears. Signal non-verbally that you are comfortable with the crying (keep still, maintain eye-contact, nod, offer tissues, pause) and also verbalize that you are comfortable with the crying (eg "Take your time – it is a good thing to cry and connect to your deeper feelings.") and let the person finish crying without interrupting (signalling that crying is important and helpful), but then ask: "what were you thinking about just then that set off the tears?". Connect the crying to what they are thinking about, "These thoughts obviously bring a wealth of emotions in you". It is safe to explore the thoughts behind the tears. Don't let a person's crying put you off asking about their inner experience. It is usually possible to continue the conversation before the crying has completely stopped.

> **KEY POINT:** Holding a silent space for a person to think is one of the main differences between active listening and social listening.

Skill 10: Empath_Y_

- Setting
- Engaging
- Eye contact
- Noticing non-verbal cues
- Accepting the other
- Self-awareness
- Echoing
- Asking questions
- Silence
- Empath_Y_

Being empathic involves a choice on the part of the listener as to what he or she will pay attention to, namely the world of the other person as that individual perceives it.

Carl Rogers, 1902–1987

"Imagination allows one to understand what people feel, who they are. It is the quality of that attention that is most important"

John Berger, 1982

The skill of empathy is very rare in social interaction. Very few people convey it and therefore very few people experience it. As a result, when a person experiences empathy for the first time it can be a profound experience – as if someone else has entered their own private inner world.

"The process of addressing emotions is straight forward" (Robert Buckman). Empathy is not: saying "I'm sorry" or "I understand" or giving advice or making a judgement or interpreting or challenging. Empathy is attempting to understand the other's point of view (feelings, experience) and then communicating that understanding. The empathic response consists of 4 stages:

THE EMPATHIC RESPONSE

1. Identifiying the emotion
2. Identifying the source of the emotion
3. Linking – making connection between the first two steps.
4. Verbalizing the connection.

---

1. **Identifying an emotion** sounds easy but it is not. Often we do not know exactly what we feel. Many sad people think they feel numb, then they realise they feel anger, before finally uncovering their underlying emotion of sadness. The words we have at our disposal to describe

emotions (anger, jealousy, pity, sadness, joy) do not really do the job. Sharing pictures can occasionally provide helpful metaphors, eg "As I was listening to you I started to see a picture in my mind's eye of you trapped in a tumble drier". The person may say "that is just how I feel!" This approach depends on its spontaneity and on a deep tuning-in to the person, when you will instinctively know if it is right to do it or not. Avoid refering to your own experiences – turn your own memories and feelings into empathic insights.

2. **Identifying the source of the emotion** involves listening to the person's story and spotting possible sources of the emotion, eg "I felt so inadequate after the episode with the neighbour and then after being passed over for promotion and then my son saying what he did". The skill of echoing can help identify both the key events and the emotions they triggered.

3. **Linking** can draw things together and can bring new insights. ("You mentioned a feeling of inadequacy and you mentioned several possible causes for it – which of these events was worst for you?") Making a connection often involves making "educated guesses" – you may not be correct but at least you are making an attempt, and this is still empathic.

4. **Verbalizing** the connection is essential and provides feedback that you are being empathic (empathic thoughts alone do little good), eg "Being passed over for promotion was particularly distressing and left you feeling inadequate and also angry and hurt - it that correct?".

This process can sometimes be bypassed by an empathic "flash" between the speaker and the listener, when the speaker responds in such a way that "both feel that they are talking the same language" (Michael Balint).

NB. The listener does not have to *experience* the same feelings as the speaker (this is both tiring and unhelpful – the listener needs to stay calm). The aim is to show you have tried to understand the emotional experience and what caused it.

People take a risk when they share their deepest feelings and it can help to acknowledge this.

> **KEY POINT:** Empathy is the most valuable relational skill we have.

Group Listening

"What I thought was __my__ problem turned out to be something else entirely – the group helped me to uncover layer upon layer until I hit upon the real issue."

"I've been pondering on this problem for months, and now suddenly I can see a way forward"

Participants in Action Learning Sets

This chapter describes a method of using a group of people (with good listening skills) for problem-solving, learning and changing behaviour. A group used in this way is sometimes called an "Action Learning Set". Action learning is a method of reflection that takes place within a group of colleagues working with real problems. The aim is to help a person to gain insights and then to take action and to do something differently. The group ideally has at least one facilitator.

The group concentrates on the issues of one person at a time. The group is for the people in it. It is for the discussion of real problems, not puzzles. A puzzle has a correct solution (eg a crossword puzzle) whereas human problems are more complex and have various possible outcomes, not simple solutions. Offering quick-fix solutions is not appropriate in an action learning set.

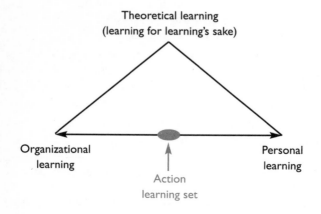

Theoretical learning
(learning for learning's sake)

Organizational learning

Personal learning

Action learning set

Each person has the opportunity to be the "presenter" and talk about a real-life problem. The aim is for the presenter to go away and do something differently.

The group provides a safe place for the presenter to be heard, to gain new ideas or insights, to reflect and to consider how these new perspectives might be useful in the work (or home) context. The aim is to use the new insights and test them out in the home or work context:

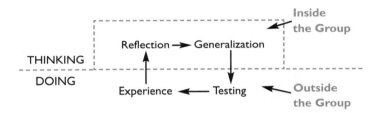

This method can work well in many organizations. It increases a sense of involvement for everyone in the group. The arrangement of the group needs open discussion and regular reviews:

- time
- frequency
- place
- membership

If new members join they need to be introduced and acknowledged – allow time for this.

Action Learning Sets usually run for several months. Membership has to be voluntary for it to work.

Having a group of people put all their attention at your disposal can be very powerful. A one-day group of 10 people might take turns so each person has 20–30 minutes as the presenter.

The fundamental questions from the group are usually:

- What exactly is the problem?
- What do you want to happen?
- What can you do to move towards this outcome?
- What can you do meantime to cope?

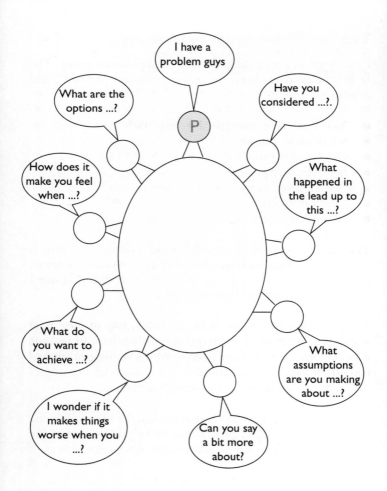

One method of feedback is for the presenter (P) to sit out of the circle for 5 minutes and listen while the group discusses his/her problems, then return to ask questions of the group.

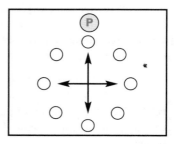

The role of the group facilitator(s)

Listening and responding are more complex in a group. The facilitator needs to keep the group members 'on task', and needs to:

- Model good listening (by listening well)
- Speak economically
- Observe the group
- Involve every person
- Feel involved in what is happening
- Admit mistakes
- Accept criticism

The facilitator needs to model good listening because it encourages others to listen. It can help to respond in terms of both fact and feelings, eg "I don't agree with that but I think I can understand how you feel about it".

Nobody is infallible – the facilitator is learning too (eg what works, what doesn't). Group members often have unrealistic expectations of a "leader". Many of us regress in groups and adopt the "magical thinking" of childhood and expect the leader to be the perfect all-wise "parent".

The facilitator must resist the temptation (or offer) of being an all-wise, benevolent guru. It can be helpful to remind the individuals in the group of reality with comments such as:

- "I think you know what you need more than than I do"
- "I don't want to be responsible for everyone getting what they want"
- "You are the expert on your situation, not me"

In very experienced groups, the members can take it in turns to be the facilitator.

KEY POINT: A group of people who have listening skills can provide a very useful forum to consider complex problems.

Ten exercises in listening

Listening skills only improve by practising them in a context where it is safe to ask for feedback and where the feedback is given skilfully – eg:

1. What do you feel you did well? What else? What else?
2. I noticed you do the following things well ...
3. What might you do differently another time?
4. What areas might you want to practise?
5. One thing I noticed was ...

Before doing the exercises come to an agreement about how confidential you want the discussions to be, and what your ground rules will be (mutual respect, not being judgemental or critical, etc.).

In pairs (5 minutes each)

1. Ask the other person lots of questions to find out as much information as you can possibly discover about them in 2 minutes – then repeat back to them what you learned.
   [The use and limitations of asking questions.]

2. Sit in chairs, back to back. One person asks: "What is the most challenging area of your life at present."
   [Non-verbal elements of speech.]

3. Ask: "What do you want to achieve with the rest of your life?" Watch the other person, listen to their answer, smile and nod and concentrate on holding a "thinking space" for them.
   [Non-verbal encouragement to talk.]

4. Ask: "What were the highlights in your childhood?" Repeat key words or phrases (verbatim) to see if it prompts the speaker to say more.
   [Echoing].

5. Ask: "What symbols or objects would you use to sum up your life?" At the end of the five minutes the listener says something like "Let me see if I have understood correctly, the most important things for you are ...".
   [Summarizing]

6. Ask: "How do you know when someone is really listening to you, and how does it make you feel?" Each listener must use two periods of silence of 15 seconds during the 5 minutes of listening (ie longer than is allowed in social listening). Discuss the effects of silence when listening.
[The Use of Silence].

7. Ask: "Can you describe an event that once caused you a lot of distress?". Listen carefully then make some educated guesses about what they experienced and how they felt. Afterwards find out how the speaker experienced your questions?
[Linking and Empathy].

8. Ask: "How would you describe your family?". Carefully watch the other person's non-verbal behaviour (posture, facial expression, hand movements, gestures) as a way of focusing on them and not being distracted by your own thoughts.
[Concentrating]

In threes (one person is the observer, the others have 5 minutes each)

9. Ask: "What things give you most sense of purpose in your life?" The observer ticks the listening skills observed during the two conversations.

Person A	Person B	
☐	☐	Encouraging (verbal)
☐	☐	Encouraging (non-verbal)
☐	☐	Silence
☐	☐	Prompting
☐	☐	Echoing
☐	☐	Repeating (to emphasise)
☐	☐	Clarifying
☐	☐	Linking
☐	☐	Summarizing
☐	☐	Empathy

Discuss the lists and the observer's findings.

10. Ask: "What is the most difficult thing for you at the moment?". During each period of listening the observer has an imaginary pause button and can "freeze frame" the discussion at any point by saying "Freeze" or "Hold it there" and can then be curious about what the speaker and listener are experiencing (eg "How did that question feel?" or "Why did you say that?" or "What were you thinking then?" etc). The observer should aim to "freeze" the discussion and be curious 2–3 times during each 5 minute session.

Summary

- Active listening is different from social listening.

- Active listening that results in helpful empathy is not necessarily time-consuming.

- External setting, time factors, social context and the culture of an organization all affect the process.

- The mnemonic "SEEN-AS-EASY" can be used as a checklist for the skills of active listening.

- Non-verbal communication is powerful. The impact of speech is not just due to the words we use, but also how we say and convey them.

- Being judgemental and getting distracted by our own opinions reduces our ability to listen.

- Accepting the other person in a non-judgemental way (even if we disagree with them) is enhanced by seeing their story in terms of their whole life story.

- Appreciating another person's story is easier if we have spent some time reflecting on our own life story.

- Engaging with a person involves establishing rapport, concentrating on their words, and observing their non-verbal behaviour.

- When mutual gaze meets 60–70% of the time it indicates very good rapport.

- The more at ease and comfortable a person feels with you, the more likely they are to open up, share their thoughts and reflect on a deeper level.

- Use open questions (starting with "What", "How", "When" and, occasionally, "Why") because they open up the conversation and enable the other person to direct the conversation in the way they want it to go.

- Good listening requires a high level of self-awareness. We can increase our self-awareness by showing more of ourselves and seeking feedback from trusted people.

- Barriers to active listening include blocking tactics to protect ourselves, such as normalizing, premature reassurance, ignoring and selective attention.

- Listening enables a person to tell their unique story and to know that it has been heard – this has been called "empathic witnessing".

- We all make mistakes; as a listener you won't always say the right thing or do everything perfectly. But the more you practise actively listening the better you will get, and the more naturally you will be able to do it.

- The simple exercises in this book can improve your skills – but reading them is not enough, you have to do them!

References

Argyle M. *Bodily Communication* (1975). Routledge. ISBN 0-415-05114-2.

Balint E, Norell JS. *Six Minutes for the Patient: Interactions in General Practice Consultations* (1973). Tavistock Publications. ISBN 0-422-76200-8.

Bendix T. *The Anxious Patient – the therapeutic dialogue in clinical practice* (1982). Churchill Livingstone. ISBN 0-443-02295-X

Berger J, Muhr J. *Another Way of Telling* (1982). London: Writers and Readers. ISBN 0-906495-68-7.

Brody H. *My Story is broken; can you help me fit it? Medical ethics and joint construction of narrative.* Literature and Medicine. 1994 Spring; 13(1): 79–92.

Buckman R. *Communications and Emotions.* BMJ 2002; 325:627

Covey Stephen R. *The 7 Habits of Highly Effective People.* 1989. Simon and Schuster. ISBN 0-684-85839-8

Elder B. *Communications Workshop* (1995). Macmillan Education, Australia. ISBN 0-7329-2851-6

Frank AW. *The Wounded Storyteller* (1995). The University of Chicago Press. ISBN 0-226-25992-7.

Griffen J, Tyrrell I. *Psychotherapy, counselling and the human givens* (1999). European Therapy Studies Institute. ISBN 1-899398-95-3

Houston G. *The Red Book of Groups – and how to lead them better* (1999). ISBN 09510323-3-X.

Hull JM. *Touching the Rock. An Experience of Blindness.* (1990). SPCK. ISBN 186355-002-X

Jacob M. *Swift to Hear – facilitating skills in listening and responding* (1985). SPCK. ISBN 0-281-04177-6.

Kline N. *Time to Think. Listening to ignite the human mind* (1999). Ward Lock. ISBN 0-7063-7745-1.

Launer J. *Narrative-based Primary Care: A practical guide* (2002). Radcliffe Medical Press. ISBN 1-85775-539-1.

Long A. *Listening* (1990). Dalton Longman and Todd. ISBN 0-272-51834-3

Maguire P, Pitceathly C. *Key Communication Skills and how to acquire them*. BMJ 2002; 325:697–700.

McGill I, Beaty, L. *Action learning* (1992). Kogan Page. ISBN 0-7494-3453-8.

Morris D. *Manwatching – A Field Guide to Human Behaviour* (1977). Triad/Panther Books. ISBN 0-586-04887-1.

Neighbour R. *The Inner Consultation* (1987). MTP Press. ISBN 0-7462-0040-4.

Nouwen H. *The Way of the Heart* (1981). Ballantine Books. ISBN 0-345-32959-7.

Okri B. *Birds of Heaven* (1995). Orion.

Pease A. *Body Language. How to read others thoughts by their gestures* (1981). Sheldon. ISBN 0-85969-653-7.

Quoist M. *Prayer of Life* (1954). Gill and Macmillan. ISBN 7171-0158-4

Rogers CR. *On Becoming a Person* (1961). Boston: Houghton Mifflin.

Usherwood T. *Understanding the Consultation – Evidence, Theory and Practice* (1999). Open University Press. ISBN 0-335-19998-4.

Wainwright GR. *Body Language* (1985). Hodder Headline. ISBN 0-340-85999-7.

Wilkinson S. *Factors which influence how nurses communicate with cancer patients* (1991). Journal of Advanced Nursing, 16, 677–688.

Zeldin T. *Conversation - How talk can change your life* (1998). The Harvill Press, London. ISBN 1-86046-662-1.

NOTES

NOTES